4

Bat, Bop, Pop!

Written by Janelle Cherrington
Illustrated by Clive Scruton

SCHOLASTIC INC.

New York   Toronto   London   Auckland   Sydney
Mexico City   New Delhi   Hong Kong   Buenos Aires

ISBN 0-439-31958-7

Copyright © 2000
Portions previously
SCHOLASTIC PI

12 11 10 9 8

Sam.

Sam can bat.

Bat the hat, Sam!

Bat the top!

Bat, bop, pop!

Hop, hop, hop!

Words With *-op*

bop
hop
pop
top